EGMONT
We bring stories to life

First published in Great Britain 2013 by Egmont UK Limited,
1 Nicholas Road, London W11 4AN

Edited by Gemma Barder. Designed by Pritty Ramjee.

© 2013 Disney Enterprises, Inc.

Handy Manny, Jungle Junction, Special Agent Oso, Mickey Mouse Clubhouse,
Jake and the Never Land Pirates, Doc McStuffins and Sofia the First: © Disney.
The stories and art herein are © Disney. All rights reserved.

ISBN 978 1 4052 6647 5
54721/2
Printed in Italy

Disney Junior

This annual belongs to

....

Write your name here.

Contents

HANDY MANNY

JUNGLE JUNCTION

SPECIAL AGENT OSO

A chance to win £150 of book tokens!

NATIONAL BOOK tokens

See page 67 for details.

Jake and the seashell house

JAKE AND HIS NEVER LAND PALS HAVE JUST MADE A NEW DISCOVERY.

LOOK AT THE PRETTY **SEASHELL** I'VE FOUND!

THERE'S A **HERMIT CRAB** INSIDE!

CAPTAIN HOOK AND MR. SMEE ARE SPYING ON THE FRIENDS.

I CAN'T SEE A THING FROM HERE, SMEE!

LET'S USE **CAMOUFLAGE** TO GET CLOSER, CAPTAIN!

I HAVE AN IDEA, SMEE! WE'LL USE THESE LEAVES AS **CAMOUFLAGE**!

YES, CAPTAIN ...

Follow that shadow!

? What's happened to Peter Pan's shadow? Find out by playing this fun game with your friends. Roll a dice and MOVE along the path. BEWARE! Some squares send you ahead and others move you back. The first player to reach the finish wins and gets to COLOUR in Peter Pan's shadow!

1 2 3 4 5 6 7 8

start

finish

A pirate hideaway

Mateys, look out! Jake and his crew are hiding from Hook! Can you **FIND** them in the scene?

Some balls have washed up on the beach. **NUMBER** them from biggest to smallest.

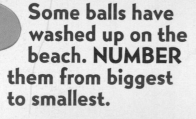

14

1 2 3 4

Piratey presents

It's a special day in Never Land, the pirates are celebrating their friendship by exchanging gifts! Can you tell what's inside each package? CONNECT each shadow to its gift.

d

c

3

1

2

a

15

Secret code

Jake's found treasure on the beach! To find out what it is, FOLLOW the secret code below!

COLOUR in the object Jake has found!

E **C**  **S**  **T** **H**

C

Up in the sky

Jake and Izzy are looking at the stars through the telescope. **MATCH** each jigsaw piece to complete the picture.

2

3

1

?

a

b

c

Hang up the hats!

Captain Hook should take better care of his hats, they've been scattered all over the ship! Can you collect them all? Roll a dice and MOVE along the path. Pick up each hat as you land on it. The player who COLLECTS the most hats before reaching the finish square is the winner!

GO AHEAD 3 spaces!

5
6
7
4
3
2
1
start
21 finish
20

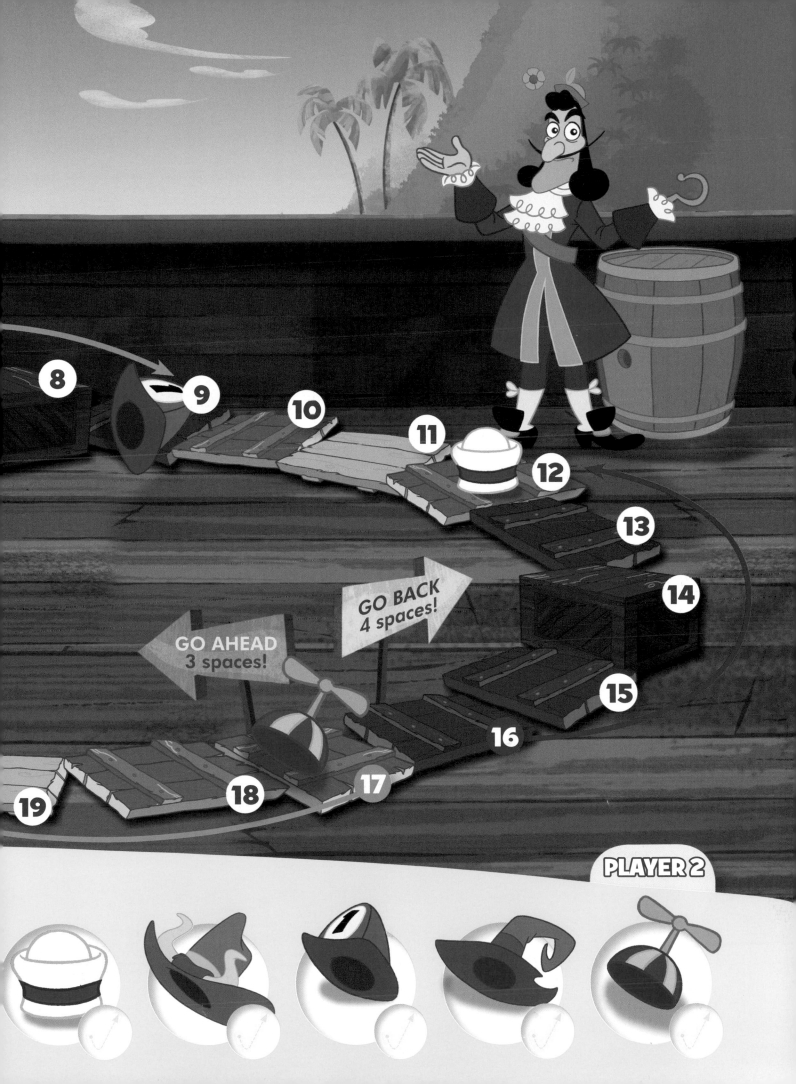

Music, mateys!

Jake and his friends have found a chest full of Doubloons! To celebrate, they've whipped up a music party at the beach! How many BALLOONS can you COUNT?

Can you FIND the pile of Doubloons hidden in the scene?

1 2 3 4 5 6 7 8 9 10

1 One morning, Goofy announced,
There was to be a hurdle race.
"It's just for dogs," he giggled,
"With a TROPHY for first place!"

2 So, Pluto and Butch, the bulldog,
Stood side-by-side, in a row,
And waited for the race to start.
Goofy called, "Ready, steady, go!"

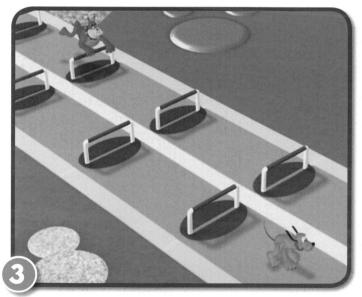

3 But Butch was big and heavy,
Which made him very slow.
And Pluto soon raced ahead,
He put on quite a show!

4 Suddenly, Pluto ran extra fast.
Something had caught his eye!
He ran off the hurdle track,
Chasing a pretty butterfly!

Can you FIND the details in the story?

hounds

5

Mickey Mouse grabbed his whistle,
And then he blew on it, hard.
"Pluto, get back on track!"
Mickey called, across the yard.

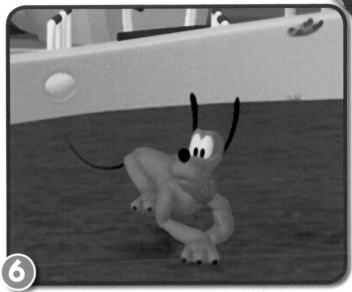

6

When Pluto heard the whistle,
He stopped and did a spin.
But would he reach the track,
In time to beat Butch and win?

7

As Pluto jumped the final hurdle,
Mickey shouted, "You'll be fine!"
And then, ahead of Butch,
Pluto crossed the finish line!

You won the
TROPHY!

8

The shiny TROPHY made them proud,
Winning the race had been tricky.
"Pluto, you flew over those hurdles,
Like a butterfly!" laughed Mickey.

Musical maze

Let's dance!

Mickey and his friends want to dance together. LEAD Mickey through the maze to reach Minnie. Now LEAD Donald to his dancing partner, too!

24

Fields of fun

? Mickey's spotted a scarecrow in this field. **DRAW** a funny face on him!

? Can you carefully **COPY** these crop circles in the box?

MATCH the crops below to the fields above. The **COLOUR** is the clue!

27

Train tracks

Mickey has made a model village for his train to chug around! Help him TRACE a track that leads Mickey's train back to the station.

START

28

STATION

FINISH

Shadow shapes

Goofy has spotted shadow shapes on the wall! CIRCLE the hand at the bottom that hasn't made a shadow shape on the wall.

30

Rainy day

? Minnie is enjoying a rainy day! Can you SPOT FIVE differences in these two pictures? TRACE over a number each time you do!

31

Bright balloons

Toodles has some colour options for Mickey! Can you help him to correctly COLOUR the balloons where they overlap?

32

Climbing challenge

Mickey is on a rock climbing adventure! Put the pictures in ORDER then WRITE the numbers in the circles. The first one has been done for you!

1

Engine Nine, feelin' fine

It was a ⭐ day and 👧 had a new patient. 🚒 wasn't feeling very well, so the toys told him to go for a check up.

🚒 was a bit scared. He had never been to the Doctor's before. But 👧 let him know that everything was going to be OK. First she wanted to listen to his heartbeat using her 🩺. The 🩺 looked a bit scary, so 👧 let 🚒 listen to her heartbeat first, before listening to his heartbeat.

Next, 👧 looked in his 👀 and ears. They seemed fine. But 🚒 had been feeling tired and his head hurt when it was ⭐. 👧 thought hard about a diagnosis.

Just then, Doc's mom knocked on the examining room to give her a glass of 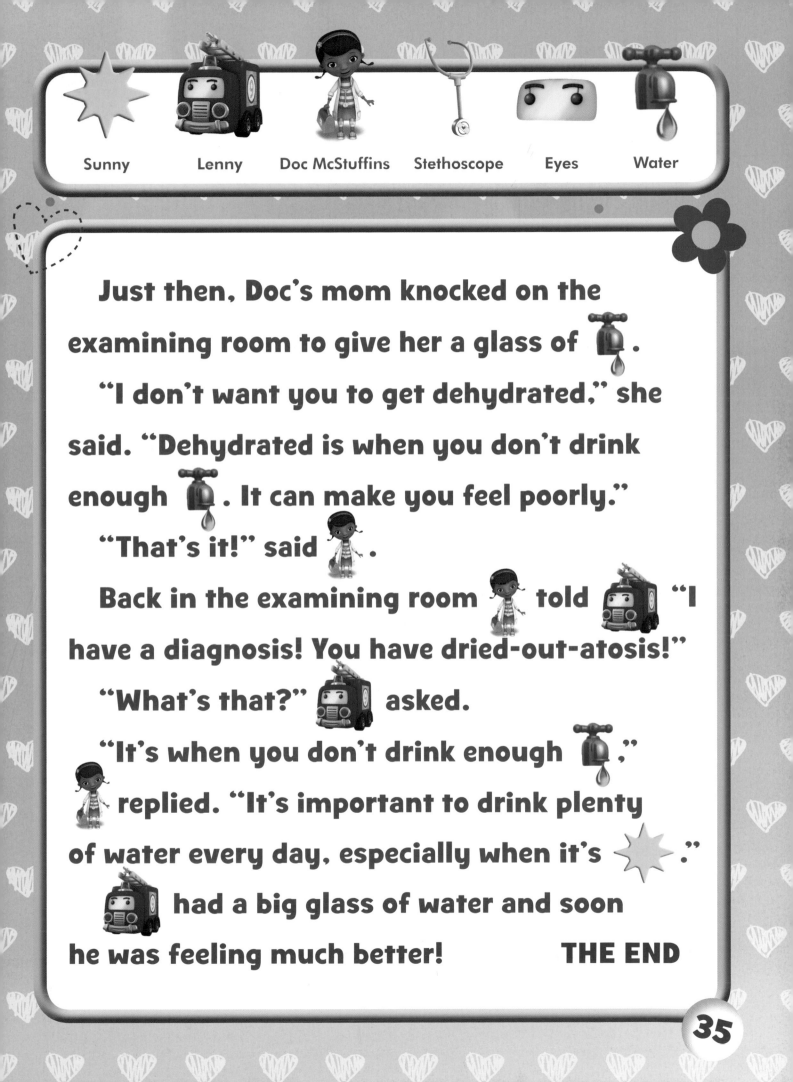.

"I don't want you to get dehydrated," she said. "Dehydrated is when you don't drink enough . It can make you feel poorly."

"That's it!" said .

Back in the examining room told "I have a diagnosis! You have dried-out-atosis!"

"What's that?" asked.

"It's when you don't drink enough ," replied. "It's important to drink plenty of water every day, especially when it's ."

 had a big glass of water and soon he was feeling much better!   **THE END**

35

Waiting room rummage

Happy together

? Can you **FIND** Doc and her friends in this grid? Their names are written **FORWARDS** or **BACKWARDS**.

l	a	m	b	i	e
y	f	f	u	t	s
h	a	l	l	i	e
y	l	l	i	h	c
l	e	n	n	y	u
a	c	o	d	n	b

Chilly	Hallie	Lenny
Doc	Lambie	Stuffy

Friends

COLOUR Doc McStuffins and her friends!

39

Examining room race

ROLL a dice and MOVE around the board. The first player to the finish wins! Tip: use coins for counters.

Start

You've made a great diagnosis! Move forward **2** spaces.

Uh oh, Stuffy has fallen over. Go back **3** spaces to look after him.

You've helped Lambie feel better. Have another roll of the dice!

Hallie says you've got lots of appointments today. Miss a turn!

You've found Chilly's missing button. Move forward **1** space.

40

Oops, you have lost your stethoscope! Go back **1** space to find it.

Someone needs a hug. Move forward **1** space to give it to them.

Finish Well done!

McStuffins Sudoku

ADD a character in the space in each line, so all **THREE** characters appear in each row **ACROSS** and **DOWN**.

Doc McStuffins   **Lambie**   **Hallie**

42

What's the diagnosis?

Lambie has a runny nose.
She has a sore throat.
She sneezes all the time.
She's feeling very tired.

What's wrong with Lambie?

She's got the measles

She's got a cold

She's broken her arm

Paint

1

Manny and the Tools were on a job.
They had a lot of work to do!
"It's the community centre," Manny said,
"Let's make it look brand new!"

2

Manny's helper had forgotten things,
They had to go to the hardware store.
"Don't worry, Tools, I won't be long,"
Said Manny, walking out the door.

3

The Tools didn't want to waste any time,
There would be children arriving soon.
"Let's surprise Manny!" Turner cried,
So they began to paint the room!

4

The Tools were in such a hurry,
They didn't take much care.
Very soon they were in a fix,
PAINT was splattered everywhere!

Can you FIND these details in the story?

44

problem

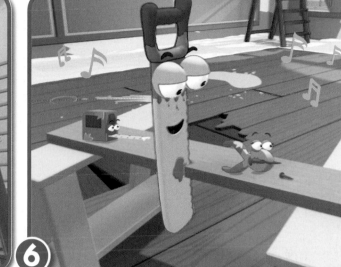

5 "What's happened here?" cried Manny,
When he arrived back from the store.
"We have to clean this PAINT up,
Then fix the chairs, the walls, the floor!"

6 The Tools quickly got to work,
They knew they didn't have that long.
They measured, sawed and screwed,
Whilst singing a happy song!

7 Soon the centre was finished,
And it was such a pretty sight!
When the children finally arrived,
They all gasped with delight!

8 Back at Manny's workshop,
There was one more job to do.
"Let's wash the PAINT off," Manny said,
"I'll make you look brand new!"

Make a movie

Help Manny make a scary movie! TICK off each of the scenes below that he has filmed! Can you SPOT a scene that doesn't belong in a scary movie?

What scary COSTUME is Dusty wearing?

Work gear

?

Help Manny to get dressed for work. **JOIN** the red dots in number order to draw Manny's cap. **JOIN** the green dots to draw his jumper. Now **COLOUR** him in!

I wear a green **shirt!**

48

Mend the clothes

Can you **HELP** Manny **MEND** the rips in these clothes? **DRAW** straight lines to link the matching coloured dots.

Vegetable patch

? Abuelito grows his own tasty vegetables! Can you COMPLETE these sums?

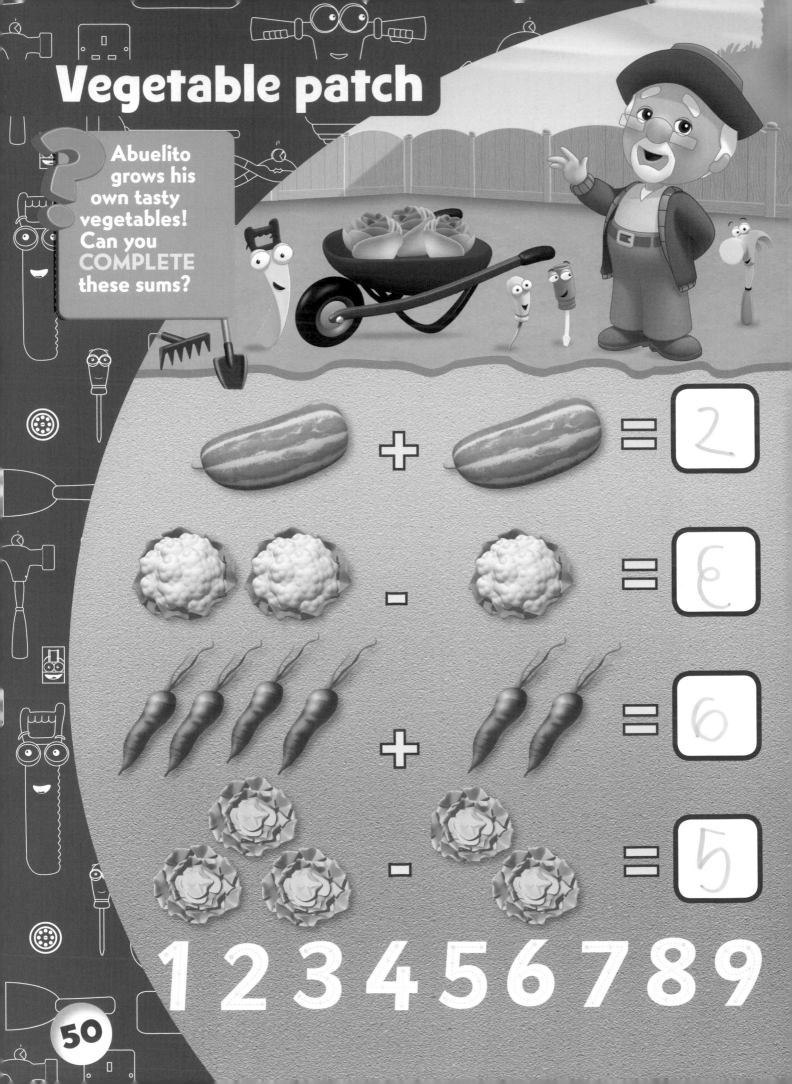

+ = 2

- = 8

+ = 6

- = 5

1 2 3 4 5 6 7 8 9

Stop to shop

Manny has stopped at Kelly's shop to get the things he'll need for the day. SPOT all the shapes from the panel in the picture. COLOUR the shapes as you SPOT them!

Nice shop!

STAR **SQUARE** **CIRCLE** **TRIANGLE**

51

Action Manny

Manny and the Tools have just watched an adventure film at the cinema! Can you **SPOT** the odd one out in each row of objects?

Make with Manny

Wood!

53

The missing

1

Crocker was in his garden,
He had lots of work to do.
Once the plants were watered,
He had some seeds to sow, too.

2

But suddenly he noticed,
One pumpkin he couldn't see.
So he went to look for someone
and shouted: "Help me, please!"

WE'LL USE MY **MAGNIFYING GLASS!**

3

Crocker quickly found Bobby,
and he had a great idea.
"With my **MAGNIFYING GLASS**,
We'll find your pumpkin. Don't fear!"

4

They went back to the garden
And Zooter joined them too.
Bobby held up his **MAGNIFYING GLASS**
To find the pumpkin soon.

Can you **FIND** these details in the story?

pumpkin

"LOOK THROUGH MY MAGNIFYING GLASS!"

(5)

(6)

"There it is!" shouted Bobby,
The pumpkin was moving across the grass.
Ants were carrying it away,
He saw through his MAGNIFYING GLASS.

The ants were taking fruit,
And lots of vegetables, too.
Crocker took a cabbage,
But the ants didn't want him to.

(7)

(8)

"They're storing food for the winter!"
Said Miss Jolly, who'd stopped by.
"So when the weather's cold,
they can eat while they're inside."

So Crocker told the wise ants:
"I'm glad to give you food,
But please don't take it all
Or I won't know what to do!"

Treasure hunt

The Jungle Junction gang are going on a treasure hunt. You can **HELP** them by completing the fun activity below.

Can you **SPOT** these details in the scene above?

56

Scrambled race

Your Jungle Junction friends are having a race by the river, but only one is able to reach the finish! **FOLLOW** the paths to find out who it is!

finish

Miss Jolly's meeting

The Jungle Junction friends love being in nature! Help Carla **FIND FOUR** differences between these two pictures.

Oso's meal

1

Agent Oso was in training,
When a special alert came through.
Isabella needed his help,
She didn't know what to do.

2

> HOW DO I SET THE TABLE?

Isabella had been asked to set the table,
A difficult task, indeed.
She didn't know where anything went!
She cried, "Agent Oso, help me please!"

3

Just then, Agent Oso arrived,
"I'm here to help, don't worry.
We'll lay the plates and silverware,
I'll teach you in a hurry."

4

They had to follow three special steps,
The first was easy to do.
They put the plates on the table,
It was now time for step two.

Can you FIND these details in the story?

mission

5

"Step two is putting the napkins out,
Do you know where they go?"
"On the TABLE by the plates,"
Isabella told Oso.

THE TABLE LOOKS GREAT!

6

Next, it was time for step three,
Laying the silverware.
"Put the fork on the left,
And lay the knife just there."

7

Now the TABLE was ready,
And the guests had arrived too.
"Thank you!" Isabella said,
"I couldn't have done it without you!"

8

Later back at training,
Oso was given a special treat.
A brand new digi-medal,
The mission was complete!

Flying fun

? Oso and his friends are flying their kites! **FIND FIVE** differences in the bottom picture? **TRACE** a number each time you find a difference.

62

Message in a bottle

Agent Oso has written a SECRET MESSAGE for a friend. You can MAKE one too!

You'll need a plastic bottle, a ribbon, a piece of paper, some cold tea and a cork.

Brush the paper with cold tea to make it look old. When dry, add your message then roll it up and tie a ribbon around it. Put it in the bottle and pop in the cork!

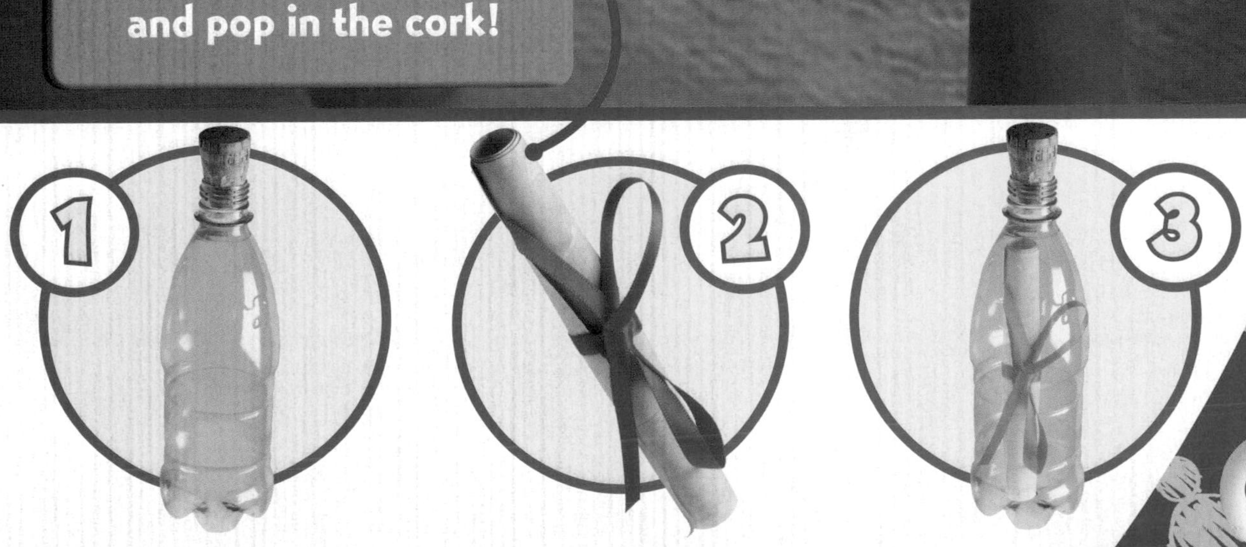

1

2

3

63

Sofia was just an ordinary girl until her mum married a king! Now she has to learn that being a princess isn't all about pretty dresses and tiaras. It comes from the heart, too!

Catch it on Disney Junior!

ANSWERS

Page 15
Piratey presents
a = 3, c = 2, d = 1

Page 16
Secret code
CHEST

Page 17
Up in the sky
a = 2, b = 1, c = 3

Pages 20-21
Music mateys!
9 balloons. The Doubloons are on the right by a rock.

Pages 22-23
Hurdle hounds

= 1   = 3
= 5   = 7

Pages 24-25
Musical maze

Pages 26-27
Fields of fun
Yellow = corn,
orange = pumpkins,
purple = tulips

Pages 28-29
Train tracks

Page 30
Shadow shapes

Page 31
Rainy day

Page 32
Bright balloons

Page 33
Climbing challenge
4, 2, 3, 1.

Page 38
Happy together

l	a	m	b	i	e
y	f	f	u	t	s
h	a	l	l	i	e
y	l	l	i	h	c
l	e	n	n	y	u
a	c	o	d	n	b

Page 42
McStuffins Sudoku

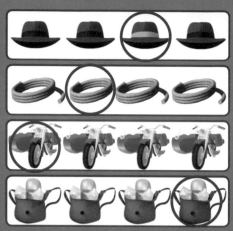
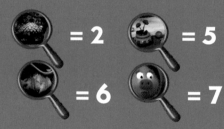

Reader survey

We'd love to know what you think about your Disney Junior Annual.

Ask a grown-up to help you fill in this form and post it to the address at the end by 28th February 2014, or you can fill in the survey online at:
www.egmont.co.uk/disneyjuniorsurvey2014

One lucky reader will win £150 of book tokens!
Five runners-up will win a £25 book token each.

NATIONAL BOOK tokens

1. Who bought this Disney Annual?

- ☑ Me
- ☑ Parent/guardian
- ☐ Grandparent
- ☐ Other (please specify)

....

2. Why did they buy it?

- ☐ Christmas present
- ☐ Birthday present
- ☑ I'm a collector
- ☐ Other (please specify)

....

3. What are your favourite parts of the annual?

Stories	☑	Really like	☑	Like	☐	Don't like
Puzzles	☐	Really like	☑	Like	☐	Don't like
Colouring	☐	Really like	☑	Like	☐	Don't like
Drawing	☐	Really like	☑	Like	☐	Don't like
Games	☐	Really like	☐	Like	☑	Don't like

4. Do you think the stories are too long, too short or about right?

- ☑ Too long
- ☐ Too short
- ☐ About right

5. Do you think the activities are too hard, too easy or about right?

- ☑ Too hard
- ☑ Too easy
- ☐ About right

6. Apart from Mickey and Minnie, who are your favourite characters?

1. ....

2. ....

3. ....

7. Which other annuals have you bought this year?

1. ....

2. ....

3. ....

8. What is your favourite ...

1. ... app? ....

2. ... website? ....

3. ... console game? ....

4. ... magazine? ....

5. ... book? ....

9. What are your favourite TV programmes?

1. ....

2. ....

3. ....

10. Have you bought a Disney Annual before? If so, which ones?

1. ....

2. ....

3. ....

11. Would you like to get another Disney Annual again next year?

☐ Yes
☐ No

Why? ....
....

Thank you! (Please ask your parent/guardian to complete)

Child's name: .... Age: .... Boy/Girl

Parent/guardian name: ....

Parent/guardian signature: ....

Parent/guardian email address: ....

Daytime telephone number: ....

☐ Please send me the Egmont Monthly Catch-Up Newsletter.
Please cut out this form and post to:
Disney Junior Annual Reader Survey,
Egmont UK Limited, The Yellow Building, 1 Nicholas Road, London, W11 4AN

Good luck!